Ollie

DISCOVERS ....

THE

PLANETS!

BY

Anya Acres

ILLUSTRATED BY

Megan Elizabeth

Far, far away to the left of the twinkling, winking star, on a little planet called Pluto, lived Ollie the Alien!

Ollie was an adventurous little alien, and as he looked up at the beautiful shimmering stars, he decided that he wanted to explore the biggest and the brightest star of them all.

It was called the Sun, and it sparkled, it shimmered and it shone.

Ollie hopped into his little rocket, and with tears in their eyes, Ollie's Mum and Dad waved him goodbye.

His
adventure
to discover
the planets
had begun.

Travelling into deepest, darkest space, Ollie saw the very large glowing sun, far, far away.

It seemed to be made of red hot fire, which sparkled, shimmered and shone.

Ollie was really excited
to see this stange, yet
scary place. He was a
brave alien. He was an
adventurous alien. So, he
decided to fly his little
space rocket towards it.

As Ollie flew, he saw a beautiful blue planet called Neptune. This planet was

BIG, not SMALL

like Pluto. On and on Ollie flew, until he noticed that thin, high clouds drifted in the upper atmosphere. With chattering teeth and trembling fingers, Ollie was incredibly cold. Neptune seemed to be made of rock and freezing cold ice.

NEPTUNE

Shivering

uncontrollably, Ollie was worried that he would turn into an icicle.

So, he continued his journey towards the hot glowing sun that sparkled, shimmered and shone.

Ollie still felt cold as he flew towards
another blue planet, called

Uranus.

It reminded him of an ice giant.

Squeeeeeek, bump, bump, bump,
sounded Ollie's brakes, as he landed his
little rocket rather suddenly!

Out of his window, he noticed that
oceans and oceans of ice cold water
seemed to surround the planet.

Brrr, shivered Ollie,
I wouldn't want to swim in there!
He just managed to
dodge the stormy skies,
before he continued his journey
towards the hot glowing sun, that
sparkled, shimmered and shone.

The next planet
that Ollie passed
was very unusual.
It was a yellowy-
orange colour, with
strange rings of ice
circling round and round
the large planet.

The name of this planet was Saturn.
Ollie noticed that Saturn had at least thirty moons, and the
largest looked like it was made of sand.

I love making sandcastles, smiled Ollie enthusiastically, *but I'm scared of getting too close to Saturn's rings of ice.*

Feeling disappointed, he continued his journey towards the hot glowing sun that sparkled, shimmered and shone.

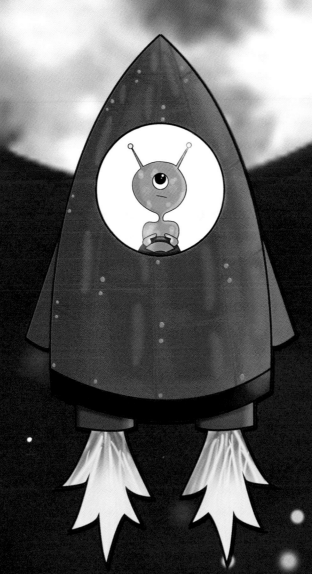

PLUTO

NEPTUNE

URANUS

SATURN

JUPITER

EARTH

MERCURY

MARS

VENUS

Ollie was beginning to feel tired, as
he flew closer and closer to the
largest planet he had ever seen.
It was called Jupiter
I bet someone lives here, hoped Ollie, as
he studied Jupiter's stripes.
Suddenly, his little rocket began to twist and
turn, spinning around and around.
He was heading towards a monstrous
red spot, and his little rocket began
whirling and twirling in the raging storm.

Bravely, Ollie just managed to steer his little rocket far, far away from Jupiter the Gas Giant.

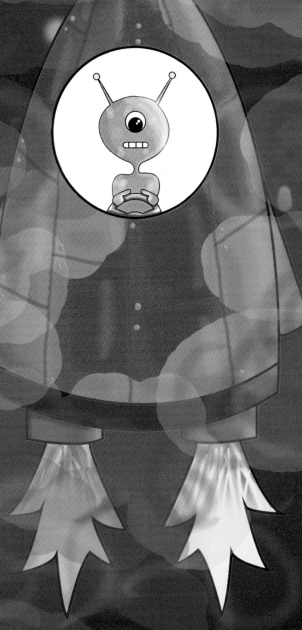

Phew, sighed Ollie, and he continued his adventure towards the hot glowing sun that sparkled, shimmered and shone.

Ollie was now getting closer to the sun.

How many more planets must there be,

wondered Ollie, as he passed planet number five, called Mars.

It was a red, rocky planet, and it was smaller than Jupiter.

As Ollie flew nearer to the surface,
it seemed to be covered with large craters
and fiery volcanoes.

Ollie was worried, and Ollie was scared.
He didn't think that he could steer his little rocket
around all the obstacles, and land it safely.

So sadly, Ollie continued his
journey towards the hot glowing sun that
sparkled, shimmered and shone.

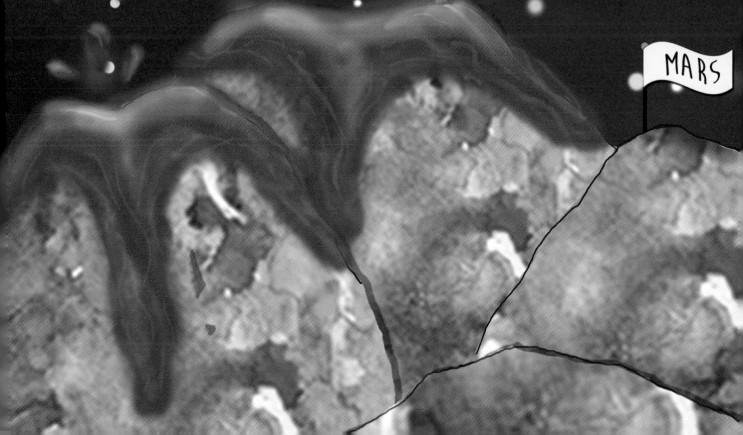

MARS

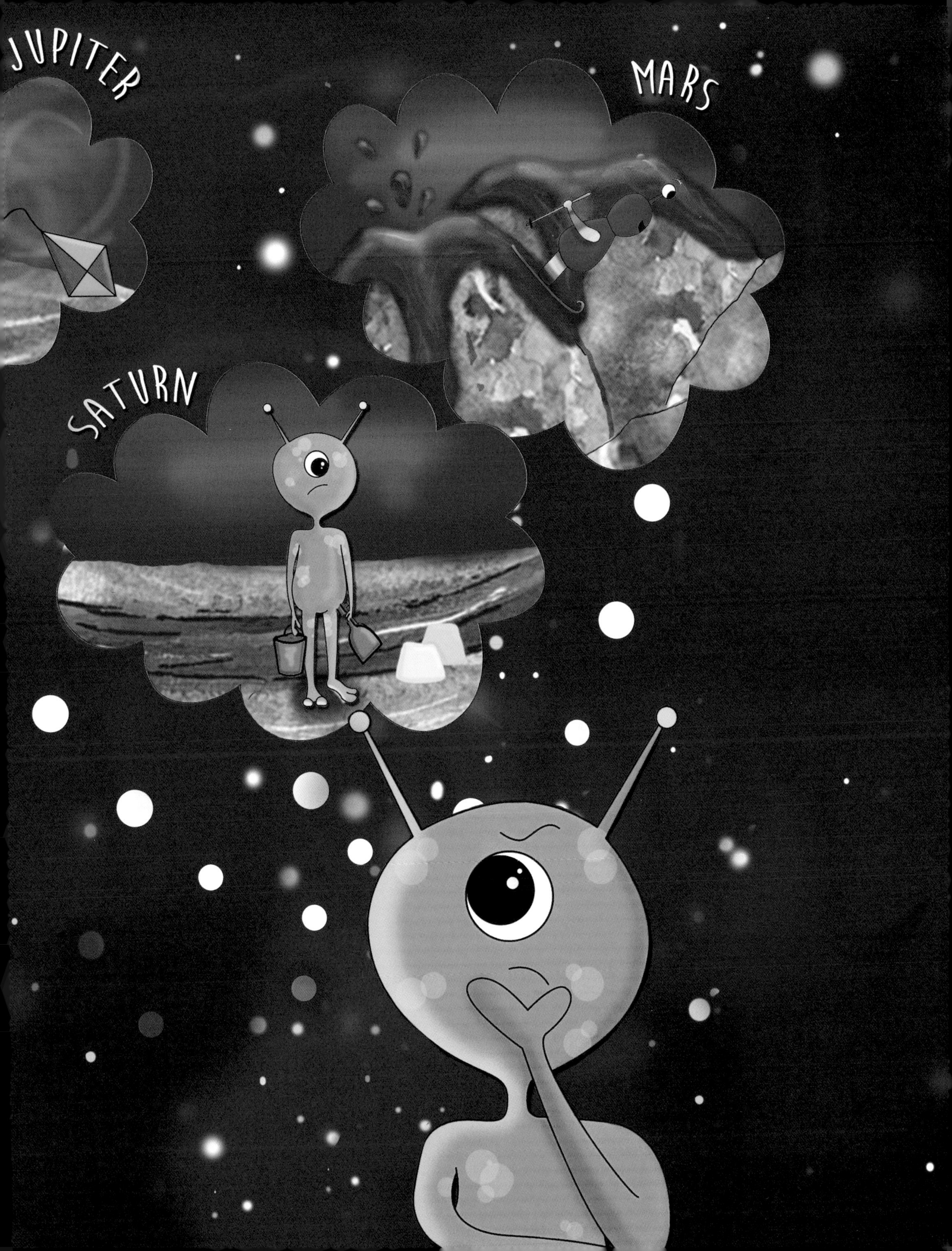
JUPITER
MARS
SATURN

Removing his scarf and gloves, Ollie began to feel warmer, as he headed towards an attractive blue and green planet. As he flew nearer and nearer, he noticed that there was much more blue than green. This beautiful planet was called Earth.

Ollie was ready for an adventure!
So, he pressed
one
blue button,
two
orange buttons
and
three
green buttons
and flew

DOWN

DOWN

DOWN

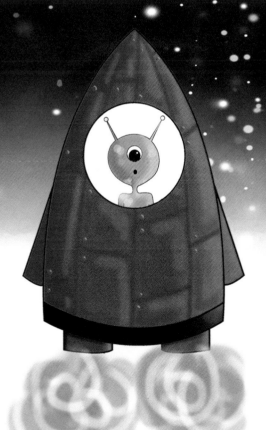

Within minutes, the strange green shapes drew in closer and closer, until the little rocket landed with a

EARTH

BUMP!

Ollie opened the door and took a long, deep breath; the air smelt good. He blinked his one eye, and began to walk on the strange green surface; it felt soft.

As Ollie looked upwards towards the sky, he
saw a large dome of blue; but right in
the centre, what did he see?
It was yellow.
It was round.
It sparkled.
It shimmered.
It shone.
It made him feel
warm and happy.

Ollie wanted to explore this wonderful planet. Many adventures and discoveries lay ahead, so he would continue his journey to the hot glowing sun that sparkled, shimmered and shone another day.

After all, there were still two more planets to discover . . .

PLANET PUZZLES

1. There are eight planets altogether in our solar system. Do you know the names of the planets Ollie didn't visit?

2. Ollie thought that the sun sparkled, shimmered and shone, what is it actually made of?

3. Imagine that Ollie sent a postcard from planet Jupiter, what would he write?

4. Ollie didn't visit planet Venus. What colour do you think it would be?

5. The first planets that Ollie saw were very, very cold, but by the time he landed on earth, the planets became warmer. Why do you think that was?